Summerdaze

The Keytext Program

Louise Matteoni
Wilson H. Lane
Floyd Sucher
Thomas·D. Yawkey

Theodore L. Harris, Advisory Author

Harold B. Allen, Linguistic Consultant

THE ECONOMY COMPANY
Oklahoma City   Indianapolis   Orange, CA

The Keytext Program was developed with the participation of Kraft and Kraft, Stow, Massachusetts.

Design and Art Direction: James Stockton

Cover Illustration: Pat Maloney

ISBN 0-8332-1047-5 Soft Cover
ISBN 0-8332-1142-0 Hard Cover

THE ECONOMY COMPANY, Educational Publishers
1901 North Walnut   Oklahoma City, Oklahoma 73125

Contents

Day after Day

Friday We Fly!   *by Jeff Kelly*   8

Keeping a Journal   *by Jeff Kelly*   14

The Best and the Worst

The Real Book of the Most   *by Norris and Ross McWhirter*   18

Book of the Best (and the Worst)   *by Paul Stone*   23

Star Run

About Stars and the Sun   *by Sima Chaikin*   28

The Life of a Star   *by Pat Lynch*   33

A Hard Day in Space   *by Paul Stone*   37

A Hole in the Sky   38

The Plant People   42

Magic Threads

Cloth   48

Make Your Own Loom   *by Ted Zalewski*   52

Annie's Dream   *by Jeff Kelly*   56

The Emperor's Old Clothes   *by Larry Raskin*   60

Keeping Fit

The Checkup *by Marjorie Homonoff and Eric Kraft* 68

Stretch Out and Grow Fit! 73
The Dog *by Alice K. Turner* 74
The Wrap Up *by Erene Cheki Haney and Ruth Richards* 76

Easy Come, Easy Go *by Mat Christopher* 77

A Race That Will Get You Up *by Elly Schottman* 83

The Old Clothes Race *by Elly Schottman* 84

Curtain Call

The Sara Monster *by Claire Griffin* 86
Sara Acts 87
The Monster Leaves 91

Your Dog — a Star? *by Barbara Friedenberg* 95
Find That Dog! 96
Yo-yo the Star 100

Punch Line

Laugh & Giggle *by Sima Chaikin* 106

Monsters and More Monsters *by Sima Chaikin* 112

What's So Funny?

Why Do People Laugh? *by Ted Zalewski* 116

Anything for a Laugh! *by Ted Zalewski* 119

How to Tell a Joke *by Ted Zalewski* 123

Watch That Walrus

I Want a Walrus   *by Jeff Kelly*   126
    Give a Walrus a Home   127
    I Got a Walrus   131

Tom Means Turkey!   *by Phil Zuckerman*   135

Buy the Best   *by Phil Zuckerman*   141

Making Money

Old Dad and the Sandwich Shop   *by April Hobson*   146
    Our Place, Too   147
    Worth a Lot to Us   152

How to Make Money   *by April Hobson*   157

Day after Day

Friday We Fly!

We work with words.

ways   gray   clay

front   fresh   free

adventures   burn   burner

thick   thin   thousands

crutches   notch   pitch

begins   humor   products

Sound the words.

away

Friday

Saturday

Thursday

Satch

secret

Sunday

Tuesday

Sight words.

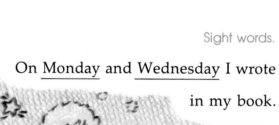

On <u>Monday</u> and <u>Wednesday</u> I wrote

in my book.

began

between

8

Saturday. That wild boy, Satch, will come to visit on Sunday. I remember him well. On a Sunday, he likes to play a trick or two.

Sunday. What happened to the window? Did Satch do it? People say I did it.

When he got here, Satch said, "Today is Sunday. Next Friday, I'm going to fly off the roof of this apartment house. Between now and Friday, I'll get ready."

"You can't fly," I said. "Tuesday, Thursday, Friday, or any day."

"I mean it. I can fly. So can you. On Friday, we can fly to a star," Satch said.

9

Monday. I have not learned how Satch
is going to fly. Today I got a letter
from Satch's brother.

Tuesday. Today I wanted Mom to read
the letter I got on Monday.

She said that I wrote the letter.
"You want to play a trick on me again,"
she said. "This can't be true. I have never
seen your friend Satch. And I have never
heard of Satch's brother."

Mom will never see Satch. But I can
see him. He is my secret friend.
"Just wait. Satch will come."

Wednesday. Satch has been up on the roof
all day today. I can hear him hammer
and saw. Over the noise, I can hear
him hum a funny song. What is he going
to do between now and Friday? Is it a
secret?

Thursday. I saw Satch going up to the
roof. In his hands, he had a big bag of
bread.

ROOF

Friday. At last. Satch let me up on the roof. What did I see? Birds. Big and small birds. Green and blue and black birds.

I looked again. On the legs of the birds were strings. At the end of all the strings was a seat made of wood.

"Get on," said Satch.

I did. So did Satch. Then he began
to hum his funny song. The birds began
to flap in time. They began to fly, and
we began to fly, too, up and away.

Saturday. Satch has gone away, but I'll
remember him. He will always be my secret
friend. I learned his trick, and I have
learned that on a Friday we can fly. If
I start work today, I can be ready by
Wednesday. And on Friday, I'll go to
a star.

Mom still has not seen Satch.
Too bad she will never see him. It's
great to have a secret friend.

Keeping a Journal

fresh frogs front

free

trying looking meaning

keeping

please plastic played

plan

proof present practice

proud

skin skull

skip

You are the only other one who has

read my journal.

I like keeping a journal. It's fun.
It's easy. And keeping one is almost
free. Before you start, you need
only paper and something with
which to write. What you write
or draw in your journal may be
a secret. Only you have to see
it. You can even hide it.

14

You don't have to write in your journal every day. You can skip a day here and there. I try not to skip too many days. When I skip one day, I try not to skip the next.

I like adventures. Before I have them, I plan them. I write my plan for real adventures in my journal. Sometimes I even write a plan for adventures I have made up.

15

Feel free to write things in your journal. I like keeping things of which I feel proud. I feel proud of this.

You can also write about something of which you are proud. You can draw pictures in your journal too.

This is a picture of me.

Sometimes I use a secret code in my journal. Other people can't read it. → △□✳️⊥♀

There are many other things to do in your journal! Can you name some? Remember, it's your journal.
Feel free. Do what you wish.

The Best and the Worst

The Real Book of the Most

aren't   couldn't   hadn't

haven't   wasn't   won't

they'll   we've   wouldn't

awhile   alone   across

themselves   herself

ends   dogs   balloons

corn   north   force

workers   worth

he's

isn't

she's

along

himself

means

short

world

ways

This story will give you something to

tell your friends.

He was gone for eighteen days.

The Best Stand

A man made himself stand up for eighteen years.
It was from 1955 to 1973. He didn't even
sit down to sleep.

The First Woman in Space

She's from the U.S.S.R. She left the
earth in 1963. She was in space for
more than two days.

The Man Who Wrote the Most

A man wrote for more than five days. This
was in 1975. He wrote letter after
letter. He did it to ask for help for all
kinds of animals. He's a good friend to
them. Maybe you'll get a short letter
from him.

Most Birds Are Chicken

This will give you something to talk
about. There are many kinds of birds
in the world. But the chicken is the
one of which there are the most.

The Most Chicken

A man ate twenty-seven birds. He did it in a
very short time. This was in 1963.
Will you ever have space inside you
for twenty-seven birds?

The Most String

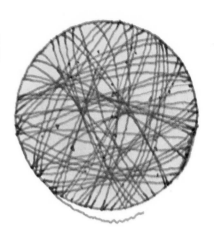

It took many years to make this ball of string. The man had to try many ways to get it off the ground. Do you think he's still at it?

The Most Talk

In 1958, a woman began to talk. She didn't stop for more than four days. In 1975, a man came along. He began to talk. He didn't stop for more than six days. He was proud of himself. It will give him something to talk about for a long time.

Most Time in a Tree

In 1975, a boy sat in a tree for two months. Two months is a long time to be in a tree, and not out in the world.

21

Most Time on His Hands

In 1900, a man walked along from city to city on his hands. He walked for days and days on his hands. Isn't that great!

Most Time with No Sleep

In 1977, a woman went with no sleep for more than two weeks. It isn't easy to go that long with no sleep.

The Word People Use Most

"I" is the word people say most. That means you'll say "I" many times. How many times have you said "I" today?

Book of the Best (and the Worst)

We work with words.

quickest hottest brightest

clear clearly eardrum

coldest

ears

fastest

hardest

longest

loudest

oldest

slowest

smartest

The Coldest Dinner

This was the coldest dinner of all time. People had to cut the soup with a saw, and the bread was so cold that it was like a rock.

The Fastest Chicken

The slowest chicken was the fastest chicken after she heard the loudest snore. She also ran for the longest time. (See **The Loudest Snore.**)

The Hardest Sandwich

This sandwich was in the coldest dinner. It was made with the hardest bread. A number of men wanted to try to eat it, but they were not the smartest of men.

The Loudest Snore

This was the loudest snore of all time.
It made the oldest house in Cold Stream
City fall down. It has been put on
tape so that the people of the future
can hear it.

The Slowest Trip to the Store

Ricky Park, who was ten years old, took
the longest time to bring bread home.
Asked why, he said, "My mom said to get
day-old bread. But all the bread had
just been made. So I had to wait a
day to get bread that was one day old."

The Smartest Chicken

This chicken learned to read. A number
of people have learned to read. But
this was the first chicken.

The Worst Joke

Two men were in the park. They sat
under the oldest tree. They were not
the smartest or the second smartest of men.
They were not even one of the ten smartest.
Mr. Green said,"Mr. Blue, why do
you have your hands over your ears?"

Mr. Blue said, "What?"

Mr. Green said, "I asked you why you
have your hands over your ears."

Again, Mr. Blue said, "What?"

Mr. Green called out at his loudest,
"Why do you have your hands over your
ears?"

Then Mr. Blue said, "I can't hear
you. I have my hands over my ears."

Star Run

About Stars and the Sun

We work with words.

hurt   burner   burst

perhaps   until

awhile   alive   across

sharks   sheep   shape

farm   cartoon   arch

channel   bubbles   allow

Sound the words.

burn

person

ago

shine

stars

yellow

white

fire

heat

28

Stars! Look up at the night sky, and there they are. How many do you see? A hundred? Two hundred? No one can say how many there really are.

Have you ever wanted to know about the stars? You're not the only person who has. Maybe every person who saw the stars has wanted to know more about them. Since long ago, people have learned about the stars. Now you can learn about them, too.

A person of long ago saw the sky as a roof and the stars as little fires. We know now that the sky is not a roof, and the stars are not little fires.

When you look at the sky, you see each star as a little body of white. The stars look much the same, but they are not the same at all.

First of all, stars are not little. They are so far away that they just look little. And they are not all the same size. Some stars are very, very big. Other stars are very small, for stars. They are as small as the earth.

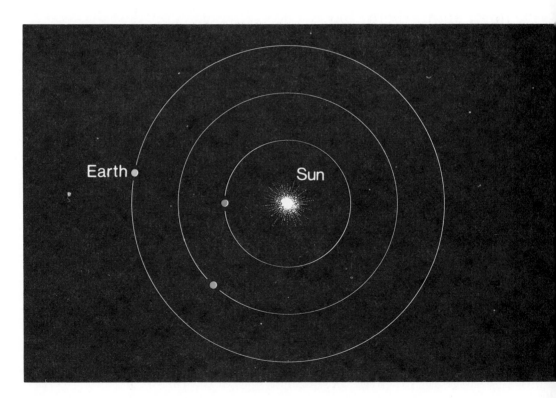

And not all stars are white.
The colors of stars show how hot the
stars are.

The next time you see a fire burn,
look at the colors. Where you see it
burn blue or white, the fire is very hot.
Where you see yellow or red, the fire is
less hot. Stars shine in these colors,
too. Very, very hot stars are blue or
white. Green stars are less hot. Yellow
stars are not as hot as these. Even less
hot are the red stars.

If you stand far from a fire, you can
see the fire. But you can't feel its
heat. It's the same with the stars. We
can see them shine. But we can't feel the
heat. And the heat can't burn us.

But this is not true for one star. We can feel the heat of this star. Its heat can burn us. This star is close to us. Many stars shine at night, but this is the only star that we see in the day. This star is the sun.

Our sun is a yellow star. It is not a very big star, as stars go. It is not a very hot star. But it is the best star for us!

The Life of a Star

We work with words.

force   corn   cords

cliff   clay   class

tiny   puppy   Harry

trouble

Sound the words.

born

cloud

study

young

Sight word.

Scientists study the stars and the sun.

33

   The life of a star starts in a cloud
of dust. Dust in space will come together
in a cloud. When the dust is very close,
it starts to heat up. When the dust is
very, very hot, it starts to shine. A
star is born!

   Many scientists study pictures of the
stars. In this picture you see a big
cloud of dust in space. Scientists who
study it feel that the little dark places
in this picture are stars about to be
born.

If the cloud is big, the young star
will be big and hot. Big, young stars
shine blue. In this picture you see a
group of young stars. You can see the
hot, blue color.

When a wood fire uses all its wood,
it will burn out. As a star uses up
the thing of which it is made, it will burn out,
too.

The end of a star can come in two ways. A star like our sun will burn up little by little. It will get small, hot, and white. Then it will slowly burn out, like a fire with no wood.

A very big star will not burn out slowly. It will blow up! When it does, it will shine like many hundred stars.

A monster star was seen in the sky in 1054. For two years, people saw it, even in the day. Then it got dark. At last, it was seen no more. There is no star there now. There is just a big cloud.

A Hard Day in Space

We work with words.

Sound the words.

thousands	mouth	fourteen		course
	whose	shoes		lose
	dove	love		above
	won	wonder		nothing
somewhere	ballpark	anyplace		spaceship
		clearly		suddenly
				done
				behind

37

A Hole in the Sky

People in the play:

Rick Mix	Woman Plant
Ms. May Fair	Man Plant
Lin A. Long	

Place: The spaceship Super Star

Time: The future

Rick Mix, the top person on the spaceship Super Star, is sleeping. Ms. May Fair is painting her nose green. Behind them stand two plants that look very much like people.

May: Nothing makes sense anymore. I have done some wild things, but last night I suddenly wanted to stand in the rain. And there is no rain on a spaceship.

Lin: Rick! Rick! He's sleeping while on watch? He's never done that before. I sense all is not well. May, do you know that we are off our course?

May: One course is as good as any other, just as long as we're going ahead. We have nothing to lose but time.

Lin: But there is a black hole just ahead! We'll go into it if we go on this way and we'll lose more than time.

May: Go ahead and ask sleeping
boy there. He alone can tell me
what to do.

Lin: Rick! Come out of it, Rick!

Rick: Ms. Long! Why did you call me?

Lin: We're going into a black hole!

Rick: A black hole? So what?
That was a good dream. The sun
above me was warm on my leaves.

Lin: That was not a dream! You do
have leaves, Rick. You have leaves
above your eyes! May has them, too.

Lin: Something is wrong here — very wrong. They have leaves above the eyes, and they don't care about the black hole. Can it have something to do with the plants? I alone have no leaves. I alone care that the ship is off course. It is up to me to fix things. I will set a new course. Wait! I suddenly hear something behind me. Say! Let go of me!

Man Plant: Don't do that! The course is set as we want it.

Lin: Just as I said — the plants are at the root of this. Rick! May! Help me!

fold   gold   sold

burner   runners   camper   matter

humor   wonder   actor   motor

answer   border   brothers   power

pull   pulled   push   full

The Plant People

Lin: I'll just take away the leaves
from May and Rick. There! That did it.

Rick: Ms. Long! What are you doing
42   here? What is the matter?

Lin: These plants took over
your mind, and we are nearly into
a black hole.

Rick: Just wait! When I get my hands on
the person who sold me these plants ... .

Lin: Can't this matter wait
for another day? We are
nearly out of time, and there
is another small matter. The
plants have hold of me.

Rick: Plants, you cannot win.
Let her go! Ms. Fair, turn
left at full speed. Give the
motor all the power we have!

Lin: Plants, just why did you
want us to go into the black
hole?

Woman Plant: Plants know of another
place in space. There, plants can
have a fine, full life. They are
not sold. The only way to get there
is to go into a black hole.

May: Our motor does not have nearly
the speed or power to turn away.

Lin: Rick, help me put these plant people into the life ship. We're going to send them into the black hole at full speed.

Man Plant: That's just fine!

Lin: When they reach the black hole, it will blow up. That just may give us the power we need to move away.

May: We made it. We're free!

Rick: Ms. Long, you got us free!

Lin: Yes, but now the motor is out of power, and our only life ship is gone. I sense that this isn't going to be a good day.

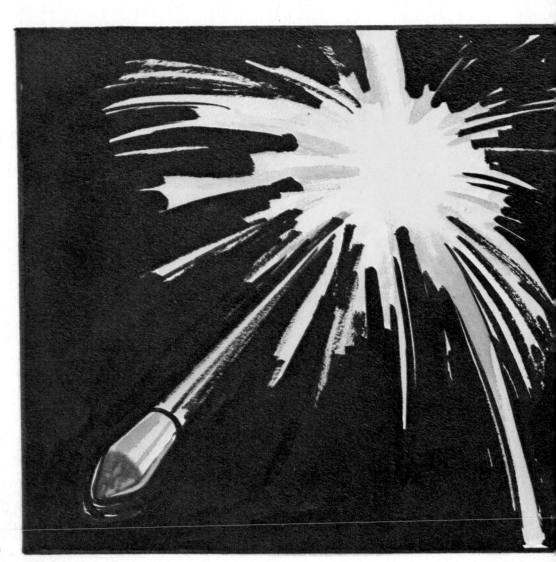

Magic Threads

Cloth

thunder   thorn   thousands

marathon   mouth   their

beneath   breath   healthy

shape   brushed   sharks

poor   fool   proof

thin

thick

cloth

sheep

loom

Today, you can use a machine to

make clothes.

Have you ever seen Navajo cloth?

48

People have made cloth for a long, long time. Sometimes they have made the thread from the wool of sheep. Sometimes they have made thread from the wool of other animals or from plants.

All cloth is not made into clothes. People make cloth to put up on the wall. It is good to look at the pictures on the cloth. Long ago, thick cloth was a help in keeping the cold weather out of the house. Sometimes, the pictures told a story. Here is a picture from a very, very old cloth.

This cloth is a Navajo cloth. The
Navajo people were in this country
long before the white people came.
The Navajo cloth is thick and warm.
It can last a long time. The color
red is in almost all Navajo cloth.

All the cloth you have seen was made on a loom, a machine that is worked by hand. Thin thread is put on the loom so that it's in a line. To make cloth, you weave wool over one thin thread and under the next.

Today, most cloth is made by big machines that spin thread from wool. Other machines weave cloth from the thin wool thread.

But people still like to cut wool from sheep, spin thread, weave cloth, and make clothes by hand. They are proud to say, "No machine made these clothes. I made them with my own two hands."

Make Your Own Loom

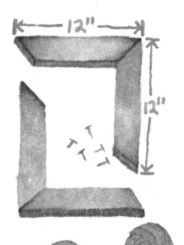

We work with words.

known knee knocked

runs beams bones

forward north record

deep broke beam

face cream main

deeds die dive

Sound the words.

knot

ends

forth

nail

nails

tie

Sight words.

That is a thick <u>piece</u> of cloth.

These <u>pieces</u> of cloth look thin.

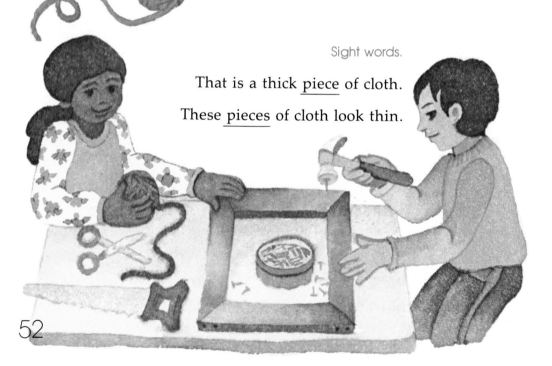

52

Do you want to weave your own cloth on a loom? You can do it. But you must make a loom before you can begin to weave.

First, bring together all the things that you will need. You'll need a hammer and four pieces of wood, all the same size. You'll also need a box of small nails.

Now you can begin. Nail two pieces of wood together. They will then look like the letter "L." Look at the picture on page 52 to see how they will look.

Nail the other two pieces of wood together into a letter "L." Now nail the ends of the first "L" to the ends of the second "L." The four pieces of wood will now look like a square.

Nail fifteen nails close together into the wood on each of the four sides of the square.

Cut fifteen pieces of thread from a ball of thick black thread. You must cut each thread so that you can tie a good knot around the nails at each end of the loom.

After you tie one end of the thread, pull the other end of the thread across the loom. Tie that end around a nail on the other side of the loom. Again, tie a good knot.

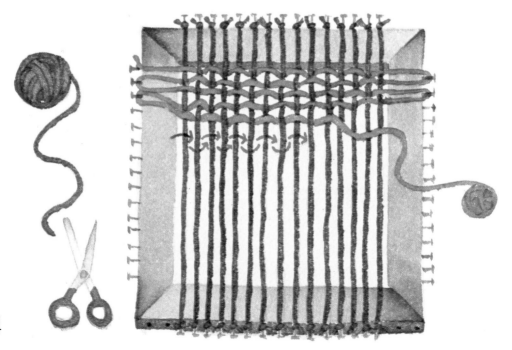

54

Do the same thing with the other
pieces of black thread. When all
the black thread is on the loom, you
can begin to weave.

Push the end of a ball of thick
red thread under a black thread on the
loom. Pull the end of the red thread
up. Now push it over the top of the
next black thread. Pull the end up
again. When you get to the side of
the loom, go around a nail and turn
back. Go back and forth, and back and
forth across the loom.

Push all the thread in from the
sides. Cut the thread along the nails.
Now you have your own piece of cloth.

Annie's Dream

We work with words.

direction   station

happy   balloons   bottom

relay   clay

advertisement   angel

Sound the words.

attention

follow

gray

important

directions

pattern

56

"The ship has landed!"

All day long, Annie heard the same thing. All the people were going down to the water to see the great ship. Even her father was going, but she must stay behind.

Before he left, Annie's father said, "Annie, are you paying attention? You have to stay at home today and get your work done. Following my directions is important. Here is the box of wool. I want you to weave a black and gray pattern for me — a pattern that looks like a cold, winter day. If you follow my directions, I can trade it for a goat. That is important, very important."

Annie took some wool from the box and
began to weave. She also began to dream
about the great ship. What would it be
like to stand alone on the ship, hold the
wheel, and feel the ship splash across
the dark blue water? She would give
almost anything to know.

Just then her father came home.
"Oh, Annie, you didn't follow my
directions."

On the cloth was a picture of a girl on
a ship. Her eyes were like the sun, and in
her hands was the wheel of the great gray
ship.

Annie's father looked at the cloth.
Then he said, "Annie, were you paying
attention? You made this cloth in the
pattern of your dream. Go on now
and see that ship while it's still there."

Now, following these directions would be
easy.

The Emperor's Old Clothes

We work with words.

moss   frost   moth

post   ghost   folk

bold   mold

Green's   Ricky's

choose   poor   proof

wonder   humor   carpenter

coin   boil   choice

Sound the words.

soft

roll

fold

child's

fool

others

voice

gold

tailor

In a land far away, there was an emperor. One day he called in the town fool.

"Fool," the emperor said, "I want to find out about the people in the town."

"That's easy," said the fool. "Just walk into the town. Then you will see."

"No, my fool," said the emperor. "The people will see my gold clothes. They will want to be close to me. They will all talk at one time in a loud voice."

Then the emperor had an idea. He called in his tailors.

"Tailors," he said. "I need your help. I want another set of clothes. They must look old, like the clothes of someone in the town."

"We will make them look old," said the second tailor. "We will roll them on the ground. Then we'll roll them again. They will not look like an emperor's clothes at all. They will not have one soft fold," said the tailor.

Then the emperor said in a soft voice, "Tailors, this is a secret. When you are done, fold the clothes. Then put them by my door."

The next day, a man in old clothes
walked into the town. He went up to
the first house.

"Good day," the man said. "I have
come a long way. Can you give me some
water and a piece of bread?"

63

He heard the voice of a woman. "My child's not well. I have only a little food. But come in. I can find something for you."

The man had some water and bread. Then he walked to another house. A man came to the door and said, "Others may have more food. We have very little. Others can help you more. But we can give you something."

The man sat down. He ate a child's size piece of bread. Then he went to another house.

A woman came to the door.

"I have walked and walked," the man said. "I have walked for days. May I rest here? May I have something to eat?"

"Come in," the woman said. "We don't have much. But we can help you a little."

The man in old clothes sat down. He had some soup from a child's bowl. Then he walked away. He was never seen in the town again.

On the next Monday, all the people were in the town square. The emperor got up in his fine, gold clothes.

"My people," he said, "I have seen
that life can be hard. Many people
have little to eat. But they still try
to help others. It is my job to help
people, too."

Just then, many people came from the
emperor's house. They set out soup and
bread. All the people ate well that
day. From then on, when someone needed
something, the emperor always wanted to
help.

Keeping Fit

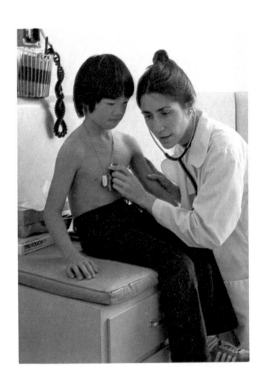

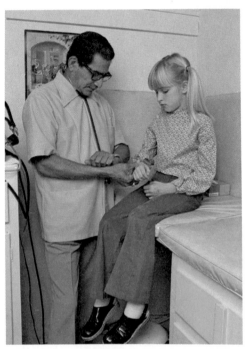

67

The Checkup

wrap   wrung

hood   mood   toot

their   themselves   they'll

beam   greatest   break

The doctor will <u>listen</u> to your <u>heart</u>.

wrist

blood

healthy

heavy

pump

tall

test

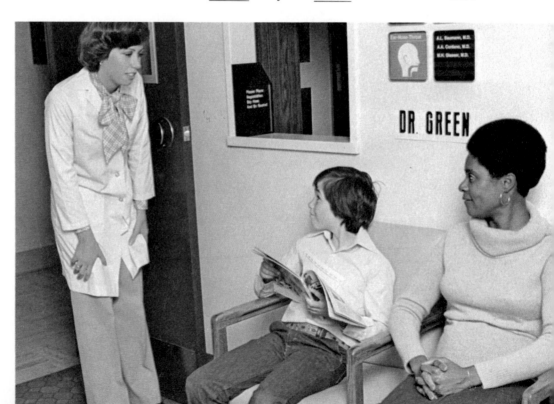

"Come on in for your checkup, Bob," said Doctor Green. "Sit down on the ground."

"What?" said Bob.

"I just wanted to see how well you listen!" said Doctor Green. "Now, jump up here. I'll look at your ears. Why, you have two ears! That's great! And I'll test your eyes. Tell me, do I have one body or two? One? That's great!

"Next, let me look at your mouth. Just don't swallow my hand! No, you may not close your mouth while my hand is inside! Now, get down and stand here.

"Let's see. You're tall, but you're not heavy at all. You'll have to eat more of that good food at home."

"Hop up here again," Doctor Green said. "Take a big breath, and I'll listen."

"With your stethoscope," said Bob.

"So that's what they call this thing," Doctor Green said. "Who told you that?"

"You tell me that every year," Bob said.

"Oh," Doctor Green said. "Well, you have a smart doctor."

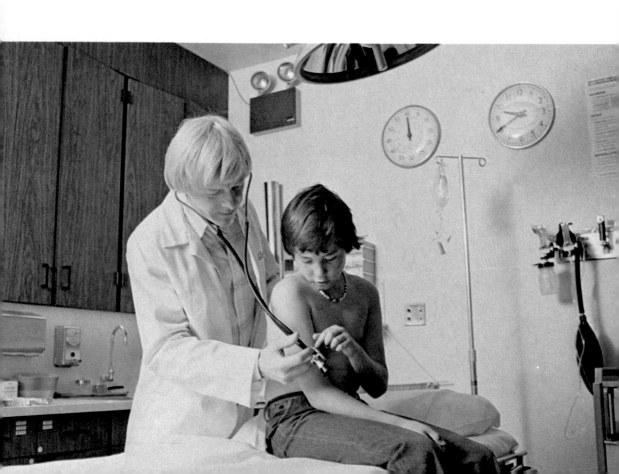

"Now, don't hit this stethoscope! It will sound as loud as a drum in my ears. Do you want to listen to my heart?"

Bob took Doctor Green's stethoscope and put it on his ears. He put the other end on Doctor Green's heart.

"I hear it," Bob said.

"Well, that's good," the doctor said. "Do you know what your heart is? It's a pump that can push blood to your body. It's a pump that is working all the time, even while you sleep."

"Yes, I know all that," said Bob.

"Oh. Well, now I'll hit your knee with my little hammer," Doctor Green said. "And don't hit my nose! Now let me feel your wrist. Your wrist is a good place to feel your blood move along inside you. You are healthy, Bob, very healthy."

"Let's see," Doctor Green said. "I looked at your ears, mouth, heart, eyes, and wrist. I hit your knee with my hammer. I had you take a breath. I know how tall and how heavy you are. Your checkup is almost over.

"But now, I must take some blood to test. I'll send it away to a place where people will test it. I'll get a report back that will tell us if you are really healthy."

"I know that," said Bob. "I have that blood test every year."

"Well, if you're so smart, tell me what I'll say next!" said Doctor Green.

"Now put your clothes on, Bob," said Bob. "Don't take my stethoscope! I'll see you for your next checkup in about a year. It will take that long to learn a new joke."

Stretch Out and Grow Fit!

We work with words.   Sound the words.

wrung   wrap

farm   barn   arm

quickest   quiet   quit quite

week

Here are some good things for you to try. Do them every day this week, and at the end of the week, see how you feel.

The Dog

1. Rest flat on your front, then stretch your back up high. Your legs and hands will be on the ground. Breathe in as you do this. Do not make a bend in an arm or a leg. Some people may think you look like a snake.

2. Let your breath out as you make yourself look like the picture on the next page. Try to make your feet stay flat on the ground. Again, don't make a bend in an arm or a leg.

Do you think you can do this every day of the week?

3. Press down on one foot. Now press down
   on the other foot. Each time you do this,
   is all of your foot on the ground?
4. Move slowly and breathe slowly. Do The
   Dog Stretch until you feel your body ask
   for rest.

The Wrap Up

1. Sit with your feet in front of you.
   Bring your left foot quite close to
   your body as you hold your left knee on
   the ground.

2. Bend your other knee and bring it up
   close to your body.

3. Wrap your arm around your knee.
   Bring your hands around to the back, and
   wrap your hands around each other.
   Look up and to the left and hold this
   stretch for quite a long time.

Easy Come, Easy Go

We work with words.

blown   clown   flown
dove   love   wonder

Sound the words.

throw

won

bee

pitch

bat

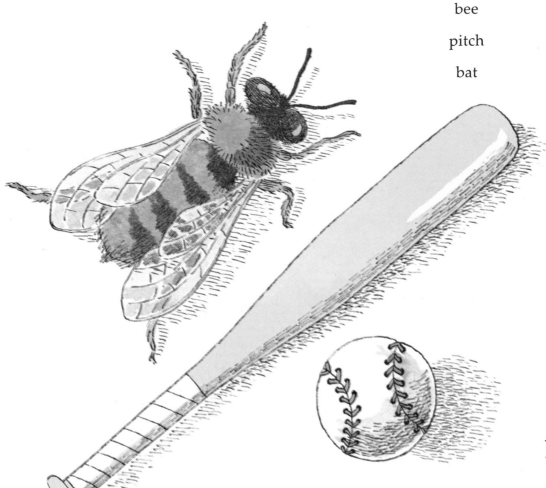

77

It was spring. The weather was warm. And, no matter where you looked, there was a baseball in the air.

One day at the park, a big bee came up behind Jean. She heard it and gave a shout. The bee came close to her foot and made Jean trip. She landed on her hand.

The bee went away. Jean got up and looked at her wrist. She didn't see anything wrong with it. But it did feel funny.

Her friend Ann called to her, "Jean, we need another person for this game. Be a friend and help us out."

"You know I can't play," said Jean.

"It doesn't matter. Just give it a try," said Ann. "Here, catch!" As the baseball came to her, Jean put out her hands, but she did not catch it.

Jean ran to get the ball.

"Throw it to Ben," said Ann. Jean did, but before the ball got to him it jumped down. Then it jumped up. Then it went from side to side. Ben did his best to catch it, but he did not.

"That was a wild pitch!" he said. "Why didn't you ever pitch before, Jean? With a pitch like that we'll never lose. If it doesn't make us the top team, nothing will.

"Just throw the ball at my hands," said Ben. "No one will get a bat on that pitch."

Jean did what Ben said, and it worked.
So they let Jean pitch.
Her pitch jumped around so much that no one got a bat on it. What was more, Ben did not always catch it. When the game was over, no one on the other team had even one hit. Jean and her team won, 3-0.

"That's the first game we have won all year!" said Ann. "Doesn't it feel great?"

All summer long, Jean and her team won game after game. No one hit her pitch. More and more people came to see her play. They had heard about Jean and her wild pitch.

A man even came to one game to write
a story about Jean. He took a picture of
her, too. Then he asked her how she had
learned to pitch.

"I didn't really learn to pitch at all,"
she said. "One day this bee came by . . ."

"I see!" said the man. "That's how you
got the idea for your pitch — from the
bee."

"Well, you can say that," said Jean.

The next summer Jean was at the park. She didn't see the yellow bee that came in from the grass, but she heard it. Down she went on her hand again.

Jean got up and looked at her wrist. It didn't feel funny now.

"Ben," she called. "Throw me that ball!"

She got the ball and back it went to Ben. But it didn't jump up and down. It didn't go from side to side.

"It's all over," said Jean. And it was. She did not throw her wild pitch ever again.

To this day people still ask about Jean and her wild pitch. But all Jean will say is, "Easy come, easy go."

A Race that Will Get You Up

Do you ever feel that there is nothing in the world that you want to do, that nothing will ever matter again?

Well, here is a way to stop all that. Get yourself up, get some friends together, go outside, and try this race.

83

The Old Clothes Race

Here is a race that is good on the days
you get up late. You will need a box
for each team. Put some old clothes in
each box, then line up with your team. Run
with the box to the end line and put on
all the clothes as fast as you can. Run
back to the start line, take off the old
clothes, put them in the box, and hand it
to the next person.

Curtain Call

The Sara Monster

We work with words.

age cage fudge

tall stall

clay club clear

peace center sentence

meaning telling walking

hood shook

Sound the words.

stage

hall

class

face

looking

stood

act

acts

Sight word.

The play practice is now.

Sara Acts

Sara stood all alone on the stage.

The big hall was very still. Then she heard a voice: "This is it, Sara, let's see the monster."

Slowly, her face began to change. Sara worked hard to make her face look ugly. She made a strange noise and ran around the stage.

The voice said, "You can stop now." Sara looked at Mr. Carpenter. He stood in front of the stage looking at her. "That was very good, Sara," he said. "We'll let you be the monster in our play."

"A monster! What kind of monster will I be?" asked Sara.

"A strange one. You'll howl, and you'll jump at the people," he said.

"Who will be in the play?" Sara asked.

"Many people," he said, "but you're the only monster. Everyone will be looking at you, so you must practice very hard."

Before Sara left, Mr. Carpenter said, "Oh, by the way, Sara, don't tell any of your friends that you'll act in this play. Tell only your mom and dad. I don't want people to know there is a monster in the play."

Sara ran home and said, "Mr. Carpenter said I can be a monster in the play!"

Her father asked, "May we come to see the play?"

"Yes," said Sara. "Everyone will be there looking at me, and Mr. Carpenter said that this is a secret. He wants my friends to find out about me the night of the play."

The next day, Sara didn't tell her
class that she was in the play, but
after lunch, she did act like a monster.
She felt she must practice.

All her friends said, "Sara acts
just like a monster! Look out, here
she comes!" At first they said she
was funny, but when Sara didn't stop,
they said she was strange.

Every day she began to howl and jump
after lunch. Every day the boys and
girls said, "The monster! Let's run!"
Sara felt bad, but she wanted to practice.

The next day, Sara went to the hall to practice. She said, "I want to be ready when my class comes to see me."

Mr. Carpenter looked at Sara act.

"You are good," he said. "You are ready to act in front of everyone. You can practice at home."

Sara went home and said, "Mr. Carpenter said I'm good. Watch." Sara made her face change and began to howl.

"Stop it!" her mother said. "You don't have to act like a monster all the time."

"I must practice," Sara said.

When Sara went out to play, her mother said, "There is a change in Sara, and I don't like it. What will she do next?"

We work with words.

pack check stick

speak bean reason

spoon noon proof

main speech meet

Sound the words.

pick

leave

poor

seem

ticket

Sight word.

The <u>children</u> like to play.

The Monster Leaves

Days went by. "Mom," said Sara, "I want to eat from a bowl on the floor. I want to sleep on the floor, too. The floor is the place for a monster."

"Sara," her mother said, "what a strange idea! Everything you do these days is strange. How do the children in your class feel? They don't know that you're in a play."

"The children leave me alone," said Sara. "They don't pick me for a game. I seem so strange, they leave me out."

"How do you feel about all this?" asked her mother.

"I feel bad," said Sara. "But I know that I have to practice. I feel nervous. I have to be as good as the other people in the play."

The next day, Sara went to the hall.
Mr. Carpenter came up to Sara. He let her
pick a ticket for her mother and a ticket for her
father. "This is so your mother and father
can come to see you in the play," he said.

At last the big day came for Sara.
Everything was ready. Her mother and
father went to the hall. The children in
her class went, too. Everyone was there.

Sara went on stage. She jumped like
a monster. She made a howl like a
monster. Everything she did was just
like a monster. Sara was the best of
all the people in the play.

When the play was over, everyone
came up to Sara. A girl from her
class said, "Sara, now we know why you
were so strange! Why didn't you tell us?"

"I had to keep it a secret," said Sara.

A boy said, "You were great, Sara!
You don't seem strange to us now."

Her mother said, "No, Sara,
you seem just fine now."

Sara said, "I was nervous before.
I'm not nervous now. And I will not
do any more strange things."

"Poor, poor Sara," her father said.
"Everyone said she was a real monster."

Your Dog – a Star?

We work with words.

whether whip whistle

letters brothers frogs

slap west rid ad

cliff tall shell

Sound the words.

awhile

dogs

fact

sell

runs

Sight words.

I liked the <u>commercial</u> on <u>television</u>.

The dog <u>won't</u> eat the food.

Find That Dog!

Harry: We will make a TV commercial. This commercial will sell Eat Smart Dog Food. Did you find me a dog? I want a young dog that can act. In fact, this dog will be a television star and get a big check.

Sam: But this dog has to like Eat Smart.

Harry: There must be dogs that like Eat Smart!

Sam: I can't find any. Monday I went to a dog show, where I saw many dogs. I saw young and old dogs, but there were no dogs that liked Eat Smart. I put some Eat Smart on the floor and stood there awhile, but the dogs didn't come. In fact, they all ran away!

96

WANTED!
Young dog actor
who likes Eat Smart Dog Food
for TV Commercial
∘∘⟩ **GOOD PAY** ⟨∘∘

Harry: Maybe all these dogs ate before
the show.

Sam: But then, Tuesday I went to the
park, where I saw some very thin
dogs. "These dogs will like Eat
Smart," I said, and I put some Eat
Smart on the ground. All the dogs
ran away!

Harry: What? All the dogs run
from Eat Smart? We can't sell this
dog food. I'm going to call the
Eat Smart people.

Sam: Sit still awhile, for I have one
more idea. Look at this piece of
paper.

97

Harry: If dogs won't eat Eat Smart, this won't help.

Sam: We'll see. People teach dogs to roll over, so maybe people can teach dogs to eat Eat Smart, if the pay is good. I'm going to hand these out.

(Late in the Day)

Harry: Did you find a dog, Sam?

Sam: Look at this dog. This dog got a prize at a dog show, and he likes Eat Smart!

Harry: What a dog! Is he a good actor?

Sam: Ann, come in. This is Ann, and her dog is called Yo-yo.

Ann: Yo-yo wants to be on television.

Harry: Sam, this dog won't sell Eat Smart. He's too ugly, and he runs funny. What prize did he win?

Ann: Yo-yo is funny to look at, and
runs funny, but he's
smart, and he did win a prize. It
was last prize. He got a check for
it.

Sam: Wait awhile, Harry. You think
ugly dogs can't sell dog food?
The fact that he's ugly makes
people look at him. There are many
people who have ugly dogs, and they
like to see ugly dogs on television.
It makes them feel good.

Harry: If you say so, Sam. Ann, we're
going to make your dog a star.

Yo-yo the Star

Harry: Sam, this is Myra, from Eat
Smart. She wants to see this
commercial being made. Is Yo-yo
here, I hope?

Sam: Yo-yo will be a little late.

It seems Yo-yo went for a swim on

his way here, so Ann had to take

him home and clean him up.

Myra: The star is going to be late!

He must not be very smart.

Sam: We must not lose our sense of

humor. Here is Ann now, and Yo-yo

seems to be ready.

Ann: Yes, he's clean and ready now.

Where do you want him?

Harry: Have Yo-yo sit over there

in front of the camera. Please

clear the stage. Steve, sing

the Eat Smart song.

Steve: To help your dog to rock and roll,

Buy Eat Smart for its dinner bowl.

Harry: Did I hear a whine in that song?

Ann: Yo-yo likes to whine with music.

Yo-yo, stop, please. The man doesn't

want you to whine.

Myra: This dog really is not very

smart!

Sam: Let's all try to see the humor in

it.

Harry: Now, give Yo-yo the Eat Smart.

102   Myra: This dog won't eat the food!

Ann: I mix Eat Smart with a secret
   sauce, and he likes it much better.
Myra: What is in this secret sauce?
Ann: Ice cream and chicken soup.
Harry: Well, can you buy those
   quickly and mix up the sauce now?
Myra: How can a dog be like that?
Sam: Let's keep our sense of humor.
Harry: Clear the stage, please.
   Let's hear the song, Steve. Give
   Yo-yo the bowl of Eat Smart.
   Don't whine, Yo-yo!
Steve: To help your dog to rock and roll,
   Buy Eat Smart for its dinner bowl.
Sam: Look, Yo-yo is going to eat it all
   up. He seems to like that secret
   sauce! This is great! Give him more!

103

Myra: Stop everything! It's clear
that this dog can't sell Eat Smart. All
he can sell is secret sauce.

Sam: Wait a second, Myra, why don't
we do just that? I mean, why not sell secret
sauce? We can call it Yo-yo's secret
sauce, and people can use it with any dog
food.

Myra: That's a great idea! Ann, can you
bring Yo-yo here again?

Ann: That's fine with me. I think Yo-yo
will like being a star.

PUNCH LINE

LAUGH & GIGGLE

We work with words.

trouble   double   turtle

bubble   wiggle

puddle   paddle

noble   fable

Sight words.

What is the <u>answer</u>?

<u>Laugh</u> when it is funny.

Sing the song <u>once</u>.

I like the <u>poem</u>.

Sound the words.

able

giggle

riddle

title

jokes

silly

walking

Let's see if we are able to make you giggle once
or twice. Maybe we can even make you giggle so
much that you laugh. Here you will find a riddle
or two and some jokes. You may even find a silly
poem or a cartoon. Well, here we go.

© 1956 United Feature Syndicate, Inc.

That cartoon uses pictures and no words. It does not even have a title. But was it still able to make you laugh?

If you didn't laugh at that cartoon, try a riddle. Try to give your own answer before you look.

What is the best thing to put in a sandwich?
Your teeth.

What can fall down and never get hurt?
Snow.

What number doesn't need to eat?
8 (ate).

What kind of dog tells time the best?

A watch dog.

What kind of dog has no tail?

A hot dog.

What is all over a house?

The roof.

Now for another cartoon:

© 1957 United Feature Syndicate, Inc.

If you didn't giggle at a cartoon or a riddle, there is still more in store. How about a silly poem or two with a missing title or two? To make it more silly, add your own silly title.

To a friend I once said, "Let's go far,
  to the round moon, or even a star."
He said, "How can I
  go up to the sky,
When I can't even drive my own car?"

Can you make up a silly poem like this?

Here are the jokes. Have a good laugh with
them.

Doctor: "How do you feel today?"

A man: "With my hands."

A boy and girl were walking down the street.

Girl: "This bus goes your way. Are you going to
take it home?"

Boy: "No. If I do, my mother will only make me
bring it back!"

Do you know when a cook is mad?

It's when you see the cook beat an egg!

What did the dog say when someone had him
by the tail?

"That is the end of me!"

Monsters and More Monsters

We work with words.

federal   banana   china

supply   zebra

animal   history

Sound the words.

several

suppose

terrible

Sight word.

<u>Their</u> cat is at my house.

Several children in a class told their most terrible monster jokes. They did very well. Are their terrible monster jokes as bad as your terrible monster jokes? Here are several of their worst jokes.

What do monsters have that no other animals have?
Little monsters.

How do monsters get down from trees?
They sit on leaves and wait for the fall.

When do you suppose you give monster food to a baby?
When the baby is a monster.

113

What do you suppose is the best
way to get something out from under
a monster?

Wait for the monster to go away.

How do you get down from a monster?

You don't. You get down from a duck.

What goes all the way up to the house
of a monster, but can't get in?

The steps.

What time is it when you see a monster
sit on your steps?

Time to get new steps.

Suppose you see several mean monsters.
What is the best thing to do?

Hope the mean monsters don't see you.

114

What's So Funny?

115

Why Do People Laugh?

116

Did you ever wonder what makes people laugh or what a sense of humor is? You may giggle when you see a clown fall down. However, your friends may not laugh at all. Maybe your friends would laugh at a joke about a clock in a tree, but you would not. Who has a better sense of humor — you or your friends? Or is it just that you laugh at different things?

Some people seem to laugh at everything. It is possible to make them laugh just by looking at them. You may wonder what on earth you did that was so funny.

Other people, however, do not laugh very much. You may call such a person a grouch.

Sometimes you may wonder if it's possible to make a grouch laugh at all. It is. Even a grouch will laugh at something.

Some people can make others laugh. They can tell a good joke or act like a clown. Other people, however, can't get a giggle, even when they try every possible way. A person like that may run around like a clown or try to tell a joke, but no one will laugh.

Would you say that you have a good sense of humor? Can you say what you mean by "a good sense of humor"? Ask your friends what they mean by "a good sense of humor."

Anything for a Laugh!

We work with words.

building   burning   feeling

arch   chalk   channel

slave   slavery   slips

state   station   steel

supermarket   wheelchair

Sound the words.

meaning

punch

slap

stick

slapstick

pun

Sight word.

He <u>says</u> that is funny.

119

There are many kinds of humor. One kind of humor is a pun. A pun is a joke that is a play on words. Here comes one now.

Do you know why the woman threw the stick of butter out the window?

She wanted to see the butter fly.

Did this joke make you have a good laugh?

A pun has more than one meaning. The first meaning of "see the butter fly" is "see the butter in the air."

What is the second meaning?

The words, "She wanted to see the butter fly," are called the punch line.

The punch line in a joke is what makes you laugh.

Slapstick is a kind of humor that you can watch. People run around, fall down, and shout at each other. A clown uses slapstick humor.

Do you know where the word slapstick comes from? It comes from the name of a stick that a clown uses. This is a stick made from two thin pieces of wood.

Let's say that Bozo has a big red nose. Here comes Mickey, and he has a big stick.

"I see a fly on your nose, Bozo," says Mickey. "I'll slap it off for you."

Slap! Mickey seems to give Bozo a hard slap on the nose, and the stick makes a loud noise. Bozo may howl and run around, but he isn't really hurt, and Mickey didn't really hit him hard.

Mickey just gave Bozo a tap, but the two pieces of wood hit together and made a loud sound. The stick that a clown uses is called a slapstick, and that is why any loud and wild humor is called slapstick, too.

A limerick is also something funny. A limerick is a silly poem that does not make sense. The last line of a limerick is like the punch line of a joke.

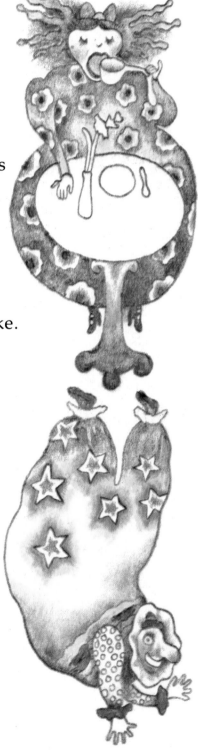

I once gave my good friend, Ann,
   A cup of hot soup from a can.
She ate the soup up,
   And then ate the cup,
And then she began with the pan!

In the show was Joey, the clown,
   He walked with his up side down.
When he stood on his feet
   To walk on the street
He didn't know up from down.

How to Tell a Joke

We work with words.

perfectly   loudly

reaching   rolling

Sound the words.

clearly

telling

Since the laugh at the end is the best part
of telling a joke, here is how to
get a laugh when you tell a joke to
your class.

1. Know what you are going to say.
Learn the joke that you will tell, and
learn the punch line well.

2. Practice telling the joke to someone.
Tell it to your family or friends.

3. Face the class when you talk, and
don't tell your joke to the floor
or to your feet.

4. Speak clearly, for if you don't speak
clearly, people may miss the punch line.

If you learn the joke well, practice
telling it, face the class, and speak
clearly, you'll get a laugh. And it's
also a good idea to pick a funny joke!

Watch That Walrus

I Want a Walrus

Be first on your street to have a

WALRUS!

★ Don't wait!

★ Send for yours NOW!

★ You WANT this WALRUS!

BUY IT TODAY!!!

We work with words.

Walter   walnut   wand

Washington   watching

pavement   agreement

soil   joins   coin

sentence   plastic   Scotland

sorry   sleepy

thousands   double

butter   murmur

Sound the words.

walrus

watched

advertisement

points

problems

tiny

trouble

dollars

ad

Sight words.

<u>Could</u> you please help me?

The <u>ocean</u> is pretty.

Give a Walrus a Home

One day, as Kathy watched television, she saw an advertisement. First, there was a picture of a walrus with a silly face and a soft body, like the walrus at the zoo. Then, a voice said, "Be the first on your block to own a walrus. A walrus has many good points. It is great fun, easy to care for, costs very little, and you can keep it anyplace. Have your mom and dad give you one as a present. Everyone wants one, so don't be left out. Buy now."

"Maybe I'll get one for a present," said Kathy.

The next day, Kathy saw an advertisement for a walrus again. This ad said, "Is ten dollars too much to pay for a walrus? No, it isn't. Sleep with it, eat with it, take it anyplace, show it off to your friends. What fun!"

Kathy said, "If I had a walrus, I would give it a name, buy fish for it to eat, take it outside to play, even teach it a trick or two. It would make me happy."

That night, before dinner, Kathy watched another walrus ad on television. This ad had a walrus that didn't look happy. A voice said, "This walrus is in trouble. How can you help it? Easy. Give it a home. Could you, please?"

"That does it," Kathy said. "I want a walrus."

After dinner, Kathy asked her mom and dad, "Could I buy a walrus?"

"A walrus!" they said. "What a silly idea."

"Could I, please?"

"Just a second," said her dad. "A walrus would give us problems. Look at the bad points. It would cost too much. And our apartment is too tiny, much too tiny, for it to live in. What problems we would have!"

"Yes, problems," said her mom. "Our apartment is too tiny. A walrus needs an ocean to swim in, and the ocean is far away."

Kathy said, "The advertisement said that a walrus is no trouble, you can keep it anyplace, not just an ocean, and it will cost very little. These are good points."

Her mom and dad watched each other for a second. Both of them wanted to say no to Kathy. She seemed to think the walrus was real.

"If you gave me a walrus as a present, I could buy fish for it to eat and make a water house for it out back. Could I please get a walrus? It would make me happy."

Then, her dad said, "We'll see."

"Great!" said Kathy.

I Got a Walrus

Kathy began to make a walrus house.
Her mom and dad warned her that this
walrus may not be what she wanted. She
worked very hard on the house.

When they saw how much she wanted the walrus, her mom and dad said, "Kathy, you have put a lot of work into that house. Since you want a walrus so much, we want you to order one."

Kathy couldn't wait to meet her walrus. After many days, a box came for her in the mail.

"This is it," said her dad. "At last, we're going to see your walrus."

"But this box is too small to hold a
walrus, and it has no air hole," said
Kathy. "I'm afraid that a walrus
couldn't live in this box."

"Let's see," said her mom.

"It's a walrus," said Kathy. "But it's
not a real walrus. It's a toy. It's just
a toy, and it's smaller than a cat. This
wasn't what I wanted."

"Sometimes an advertisement doesn't
mean what you think it means," her dad
said. "I did something like this when I
was young, too. Only I had 100 pieces to
a plane instead of a whole plane." They
began to laugh as her dad gave her a
hug.

Kathy then began to think about the
first ad she saw on television. It said
that the walrus would be easy to care for,
it could live anyplace, and it wasn't
going to cost a lot. That was all true.

The second ad said that she could
sleep with her walrus and take it anyplace
she wanted. All that was true, too.
Yet her walrus wasn't real. It was a toy
a lot smaller than a tiny cat.

The next day, Kathy took a survey of
the other boys and girls in her apartment
house. The ad had said that a lot of boys
and girls would want the walrus. But her
survey showed that only the boys and
girls much smaller than Kathy wanted it.
"Well," she said, "I learned something.
An advertisement may be true, but it
can still trick you."

Tom Means Turkey!

We work with words.

donkey money honey

cool booth

eagle break

thousands troup

Fred frogs

Sight words.

Sound the words.

turkey

proof

steak

coupon

fresh

main

Tom's

The <u>English</u> people live far away.

We <u>should</u> have turkey for dinner.

Tom's Turkeys are Fresh
Tom's Turkeys are Good

135

For a long time, Tom had to live with
problems — turkeys.

Tom has a turkey farm, and today Tom's
fresh turkeys are the best in the world.
But at one time, no one had ever heard
of Tom, or his turkeys.

How was he to sell some turkeys, soon?
There were turkeys in his bed. Turkeys
walked all over the table when he ate.
When he went to sit down, a turkey
would be there.

Sometimes he would wonder, "Who runs
this farm, me or the turkeys?"

Tom said, "The main thing is that
most people don't know about my turkeys."

137

So Tom wrote an ad. It said, "Tom's Turkeys Are Fresh! Tom's Turkeys Are Good!" But Tom put the ad up in his house, so no one saw it.

Then one day Tom saw an ad for Happy Mix on TV. It made him want some to eat.

"Say, that's it!" said Tom. "I'll go on TV to sell my turkeys. I'll tell people that they can bring back the turkey if they don't like it. That should be proof that my turkeys are good and fresh."

Tom also wanted to say that turkey is a good buy. He would show that it would cost a family less to eat turkey than to eat steak.

Tom said, "And to make it cost even less, I'll give a coupon with each turkey! But the main thing is to give people the facts!"

For the next week Tom worked very hard on his ad. He wanted to give people proof his turkeys were a good buy.

He also wanted to say his ad in English and Spanish, so he could talk to more people. He could reach people who speak English and people who speak Spanish.

Then the big day came. Tom was ready, but he was nervous.

Then the television people were ready.

"Take one," said a woman. Tom looked at the TV camera.

139

"Turkey!" said Tom. "Let's talk turkey. For dinner, turkey can't be beat. You can make a turkey dinner for a big family for a lot less than steak. Yes, turkey is a good buy, but to make it even better, a coupon comes with every Tom's Turkey. My turkeys are so good that I put my name on them. So if the turkey you buy isn't fresh, talk to me, Tom. I will take care of it for you."

Many people saw Tom's ad on TV. They heard it in Spanish and in English. Tom sold so many turkeys that he had his house to himself. And today when you hear turkey, Tom comes to mind.

Buy the Best

share   careful   dare

understand   somewhere   seaweed

wagon   vocal

compare

supermarket

products

I <u>believe</u> it.

<u>Half</u> of this is for you.

141

When you go to the supermarket, why do you buy something? Was it in an ad on TV? Did your friend tell you? Or is it the picture on the box? How do people get you to buy?

Let's say that a TV star in an ad says, "I use Frog Cream. It makes my skin soft." Wouldn't you want to use Frog Cream and be like the star? The Frog Cream people hope so. This is one way that people try to get you to buy. They hope that you will want to use what TV stars say they use.

Maybe they may try this way. If everyone likes something, wouldn't you say that it must be good? If a TV commercial says that everyone likes to eat Happy Mix, wouldn't you like to eat some, too? The Happy Mix people hope so.

Most of the time what a commercial says will be true. Sometimes what is said may be only half true. Or an ad may bend what is true so that the products seem better than they are. (Remember the walrus?)

Suppose that a television commercial says that Super Turkey is big and fresh and doesn't cost as much as other turkeys. Or suppose the ad says that half the people in the United States eat Super Turkey. Or perhaps a TV star says that she has Super Turkey for dinner every night. How much of that can you believe?

If an ad seems half true, or if you don't believe it, you can go to the supermarket and compare the products. Compare Super Turkey and the other kinds of turkey.

143

Perhaps Super Turkeys are half the size of the others and cost twice as much. You wouldn't buy Super Turkey then, would you?

Next time you see an ad, ask yourself the following:

1. How do these products compare with other products of the same kind?
2. Do I want this because an ad says that everyone has one?
3. Do I want this because a TV star has it or uses it?

When you go to the supermarket, buy what you believe is best.

Making Money

Old Dad and the Sandwich Shop

We work with words.

worry	worse	worm
force	snorkel	north
	soil	point
filled	dusted	burned

Sound the words.

worth

horse

coin

turned

lucky

Our Place, Too

Old Dad, we called him. He was about as big as a tank truck. And he had a laugh about that big, too. Old Dad ran a sandwich shop at Second and Vine.

Old Dad and his Sandwich Shop were a way of life on Second Street, like the noise and the cars and the night life.

Man, I just couldn't picture Second Street without Old Dad and the Sandwich Shop. That shop was worth a lot to us.

147

We would all go in there after
school — me, and Legs Brown, and Horse
Face Green, and Lucky Joey English, and
Motor Mouth Carpenter, and Sam Something.
(I never did know her last name. But
what is a last name between friends?)

We would all hit the place about 3:30.
And Old Dad would always say, "Oh,
no! Not you again." And he would
laugh that big tank truck laugh of his.

He would stick a coin (his own coin)
in the music box. He always turned it
up loud. Boy. He must have put
about $600 worth of music on. Just
for us.

Maybe it was that he didn't have any
children of his own. He didn't think
much about it. After all, Old Dad was
Old Dad. He just did things like that.

Well, as I said on the page before
last, we would all get together at
Old Dad's about 3:30, and maybe have
a sandwich or something. Dad's Sandwich
Shop had the only color television
on Second Street. He got it when he
turned out to have the lucky number
at a Fun City dance. So we would
always watch the baseball game over
at Dad's.

But most of all, Dad's Sandwich Shop was our place to horse around. See, Old Dad didn't jump us for that the way they sometimes had to do at school. "There is a place to study and a place to horse around," Old Dad would say. "School is the place to study. This is a place to horse around. Just don't run off the paying people."

We wouldn't think of it. For Old Dad's was "Our Place." He had been there as long as anyone could remember. And he would always be there.

Wouldn't he?

151

<u>Worth a Lot to Us</u>

It happened the night of the Second
Street Fire. That wasn't a big fire,
as fires go. But it got to a body shop,
a supermarket, and — wouldn't you know
it — Old Dad's, before they could put
it out.

The Sandwich Shop wasn't hit as hard
as the rest. But the big store front
window was out. One wall was black.
There was water all over everything.
And the music box didn't work. Old
Dad took it hard.

153

They said $600 would fix it up. But who had $600? Not Old Dad. And not us. How to get it?

"Maybe we could get on a television game show," said Sam. "And win!"

"Oh, come on," said Legs Brown. "You have to know something to win on a television game show. We're not even in middle school yet. What do we know?"

"Well, we know a television game show is out," said Joey English. "Maybe we could sell my baseball cards," said Horse Face.

"I could sell the Brooklyn Bridge," said Motor Mouth. "A lot of people sell the Brooklyn Bridge when they get hard up."

So much for Motor Mouth.

But we didn't have to sell a
skateboard, baseball cards, or the
Brooklyn Bridge.

It was Sam Something who came up with
a real answer. By Saturday, we were all
set up.

WE CLEAN ANYTHING
FiX YOUR BIKE FLat
WASH YOUR CAR- YOUR FLOOR
YOUR DOG -YOUR CAT
WALK YOUR DOG - YOUR CAT
ALSO WE TEACH SKATEBOARD
AND YO-Yo WE DO IT IN SPANISH
AND OR ENGLISH
IF YOU need it WE DO IT
$1.00

Well, we found out fast that, in our
neighborhood, no one was about to pay
for any of that.

But that didn't stop us. You know
what we did? We went to another
neighborhood. And that's when we
got lucky.

Oh, we had problems, of course.
And it took some time. But I will
make a long story short. 380 dogs,
219 chores, and 1 cat, and we had $600.
Us!!!

The first thing Old Dad did (after
he let out that tank truck laugh of
his), was fix the music box. But we
always put the coin in now.

You know, I just can't picture Second
Street without Old Dad and the Sandwich
Shop.

That shop is worth a lot to us.

How to Make Money

The paper money we use does not grow on a tree, you know. It is made. This is how.

First, people draw the pictures you see on the money. A machine will take the pictures and make more. Then a press will print the pictures on paper. They print many pieces of paper money on each big piece of paper.

Paper for money is like no other paper. It has red and blue thread in it. The thread is so small you can't see it. But it's there. If the thread is not there, it's not real money.

157

Here you see someone check the money.
If a piece is not perfect, out it goes.

The rest of the money goes out into
the world. With any luck, you may
get a little of it.

ACKNOWLEDGMENTS

For permission to adapt and reprint copyrighted materials, grateful acknowledgment is made to the following publishers:

The Bobbs-Merrill Co., Inc., for "The Wrap Up," an adaptation of "The Deer" from *Yoga for Children* by Erene Cheki Haney and Ruth Richards. Copyright © 1973 by Erene Cheki Haney and Ruth Richards. Illustrations copyright © 1973 by Betty Schilling. Reprinted by permission of The Bobbs-Merrill Co., Inc.

Little, Brown and Company, for "Easy Come, Easy Go" adapted from *Lucky Seven:* Sports Stories by Matt Christopher. Copyright © 1962 by the Standard Publishing Company. Used by permission of Little, Brown and Co.

Sterling Publishing Company, Inc., for "The Real Book of the Most" adapted from the *Guinness Book of World Records.* Copyright © 1977 by Sterling Publishing Company, Inc. Used by permission.

Franklin Watts, Inc., for "The Dog" adapted from *Yoga for Beginners* by Alice K. Turner. Copyright © 1973 by Alice K. Turner. Used by permission of the publisher.

Grateful acknowledgment is made to the following for reproduction of photographs and color transparencies on the pages indicated:

Dennis Anderson 7, 27, 47, 49, 50, 51, 67, 70, 85, 87, 88, 89, 90, 92, 93, 94, 115, 116, 117, 123, 124, 145; The Bettmann Archive, Inc. 51; California Institute of Technology, Carnegie Institution of Washington, and Hale Observatories 28, 33, 34, 35; Museum of the American Indian, Heye Foundation 50.

Grateful acknowledgment is made to the following for illustrations on the pages indicated:

Tom Adams 73, 75, 76; Ellen Blonder 60, 63, 65, 66; April Funcke 18, 20, 21, 23, 24, 112, 113, 114, 125, 146, 147, 148, 149, 150, 151, 152, 153, 155, 156, 157; Sue Gilmour 52, 54; Heather King 68, 70, 126, 128, 129, 130; Mary Knowles 8, 9, 10, 11, 12, 13; Pat Maloney 17, 83, 84, 119, 120, 122, 135, 136, 137, 138, 139; Steve Reoutt 77, 80, 81, 82, 95, 96, 97, 98, 99, 100, 101, 102, 103, 104, 141, 143, 144; Phil Smith 37, 39, 40, 42, 43, 45, 46, 56, 58, 59; James Stockton 30, 32; Connie Warton 14, 15, 16.